Myth[...]

[...]

Paul Broadbent

Aurora is a griffin. She can fly high above the Enchanted Forest and often takes Finn for a ride.

Sparkle, Gem, Dusty and *Firefly* are four playful fairies who live in the bluebell fields.

Professor Willow is a wise old gentleman, who loves to gather facts for his Book of Knowledge.

Gribbit and *Periwinkle* are naughty pixies who play tricks on the fairies with some help from their bug friends.

Finn is an elf prince, who is mastering the art of living in harmony with nature before he becomes king.

Pearl is a unicorn who lives by the Lake of Wisdom. She loves to travel and shares her stories with the forest creatures.

Welcome to the Enchanted Forest!

Contents

Letts

Numbers to 100

I am Professor Willow. When I was a young student, I started by learning all the numbers to 100. These are the numbers to 99.

100 (one hundred) is the number after 99.

0	1	2	3	4	5	6	7	8	9
10	11	12	13	14	15	16	17	18	19
20	21	22	23	24	25	26	27	28	29
30	31	32	33	34	35	36	37	38	39
40	41	42	43	44	45	46	47	48	49
50	51	52	53	54	55	56	57	58	59
60	61	62	63	64	65	66	67	68	69
70	71	72	73	74	75	76	77	78	79
80	81	82	83	84	85	86	87	88	89
90	91	92	93	94	95	96	97	98	99

Use these to help you read and write the numbers. It is as easy as 1-2-3!

20 twenty	30 thirty	40 forty	50 fifty
60 sixty	70 seventy	80 eighty	90 ninety

Join each word to the matching number by drawing a line. No time like the present!

a eighty
b twelve
c thirty
d twenty-six
e seventy-five
f ninety-one
g nineteen
h fifty-seven

12   30
75   80   57
91
19   26

2 **Now write the missing numbers on these number grids.**

a

20	21		23
30		32	33
	41	42	

b

76		78	79
86	87		89
	97	98	

3 **Tick-tock! Write the missing middle numbers.**

a

43 44 ☐ 46 47

c

67 68 ☐ 70 71

b 8 9 ☐ 11 12

d 48 49 ☐ 51 52

Willow's Quest

Write each number as a word to complete this puzzle. If at first you do not succeed, try, try again!

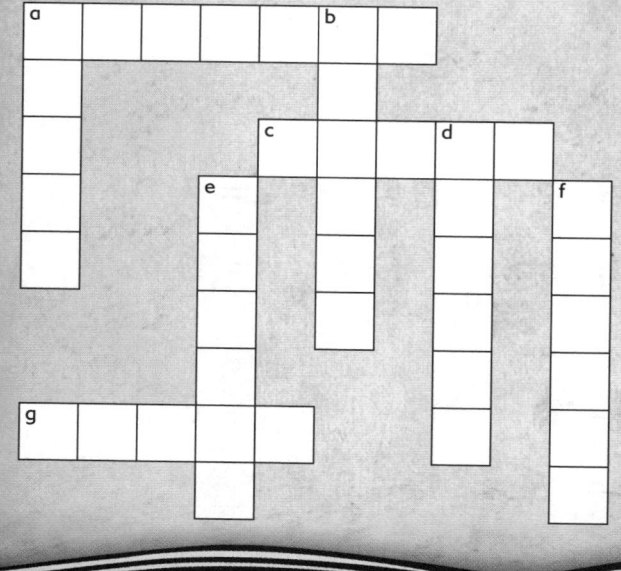

Across	Down
a 70	a 60
c 50	b 30
g 40	d 20
	e 90
	f 80

Put the sticker of my Book of Knowledge on the map at the back of this book.

3

Addition and subtraction

We are Periwinkle and Gribbit. We shall use our magic arrows to show you how addition and subtraction are connected. Let's get busy!

Look at this addition and subtraction trio for 12, 4 and 8.

$$4 + 8 = 12 \qquad 12 - 4 = 8$$
$$8 + 4 = 12 \qquad 12 - 8 = 4$$

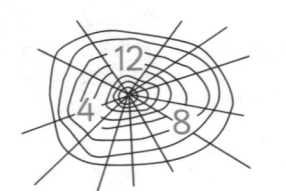

1 Can you complete the addition and subtraction facts for each trio, smarty-pants?

a

$$5 + 9 = \boxed{} \qquad \boxed{} - 5 = 9$$
$$9 + 5 = \boxed{} \qquad \boxed{} - 9 = 5$$

b

$$6 + \boxed{} = 13 \qquad 13 - \boxed{} = 7$$
$$13 - \boxed{} = 6 \qquad 7 + \boxed{} = 13$$

c

$$\boxed{} + 8 = 15 \qquad 15 - \boxed{} = 8$$
$$8 + \boxed{} = 15 \qquad 15 - 8 = \boxed{}$$

2 Try these pongy problems. Use the subtractions to help find the missing numbers in the additions.

a 11 − 3 = ☐

☐ + 3 = 11

b 12 − 7 = ☐

7 + ☐ = 12

c 17 − 9 = ☐

☐ + 9 = 17

d 16 − 5 = ☐

5 + ☐ = 16

3 Write the addition and subtraction facts for each of these.

a 4 + ☐ = ☐

9 − ☐ = ☐

b 8 + ☐ = ☐

13 − ☐ = ☐

c 7 + ☐ = ☐

14 − ☐ = ☐

d 6 + ☐ = ☐

18 − ☐ = ☐

Willow's Quest

Choose a number to complete each fact. Only use each number once. Bugalicious!

2   3   4   5   6   7

4 + ☐ = 11   12 − ☐ = 6   ☐ + 13 = 15

☐ − 3 = 2   7 + ☐ = 10   18 − ☐ = 14

Put the sticker of the mice fishing on the map.

Counting patterns

I am Pearl. On my travels through the Enchanted Forest, I have seen many interesting ways to count. If you count in 2s, 5s or 10s, you can make number patterns!

+2   +2   +2   +2

15   17   19   [ ]   23

The difference between each number is 2. The missing number is 21.

-10   -10   -10   -10

64   54   44   34   [ ]

The difference between each number is 10. The missing number is 24.

Take your time and write the next three numbers.

a +2 7 9 11 13 ( ) ( ) ( )

b +2 46 48 50 52 ( ) ( ) ( )

c +5 8 13 18 23 ( ) ( ) ( )

d +5 62 67 72 77 ( ) ( ) ( )

e +10 5 15 25 35 ( ) ( ) ( )

f +10 39 49 59 69 ( ) ( ) ( )

2 **Look carefully and continue these number patterns.**

○ Count in 2s and circle each number.

✗ Count in 5s and cross each number.

╲ Count in 10s and colour each number yellow.

1	②	3	④	5̶	⑥	7	⑧	9	⑩
11	12	13	14	15	16	17	18	19	20
21	22	23	24	25	26	27	28	29	30
31	32	33	34	35	36	37	38	39	40

3 **Use the magic within you to write in the missing numbers.**

a 91 93 ( ) 97 99

b 55 ( ) 75 85 95

c 26 36 46 56 ( )

d ( ) 32 34 36 38

e 47 52 57 ( ) 67

f 1 ( ) 21 31 41

Willow's Quest

Use counting patterns to find the path for each frog across the lake. Swish, swish!

+ 10
+ 2
+ 5

Start

18

28 38 48 26 63 68

20 28 24 58 28 73 78

23 22 33 68 53 30 32

38 43 48 78 88 98

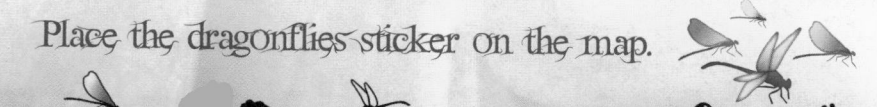

Place the dragonflies sticker on the map.

7

2D shapes

We are Gem and Sparkle. We will soon swirl some fairy dust over these shapes!

2D shapes are flat shapes.

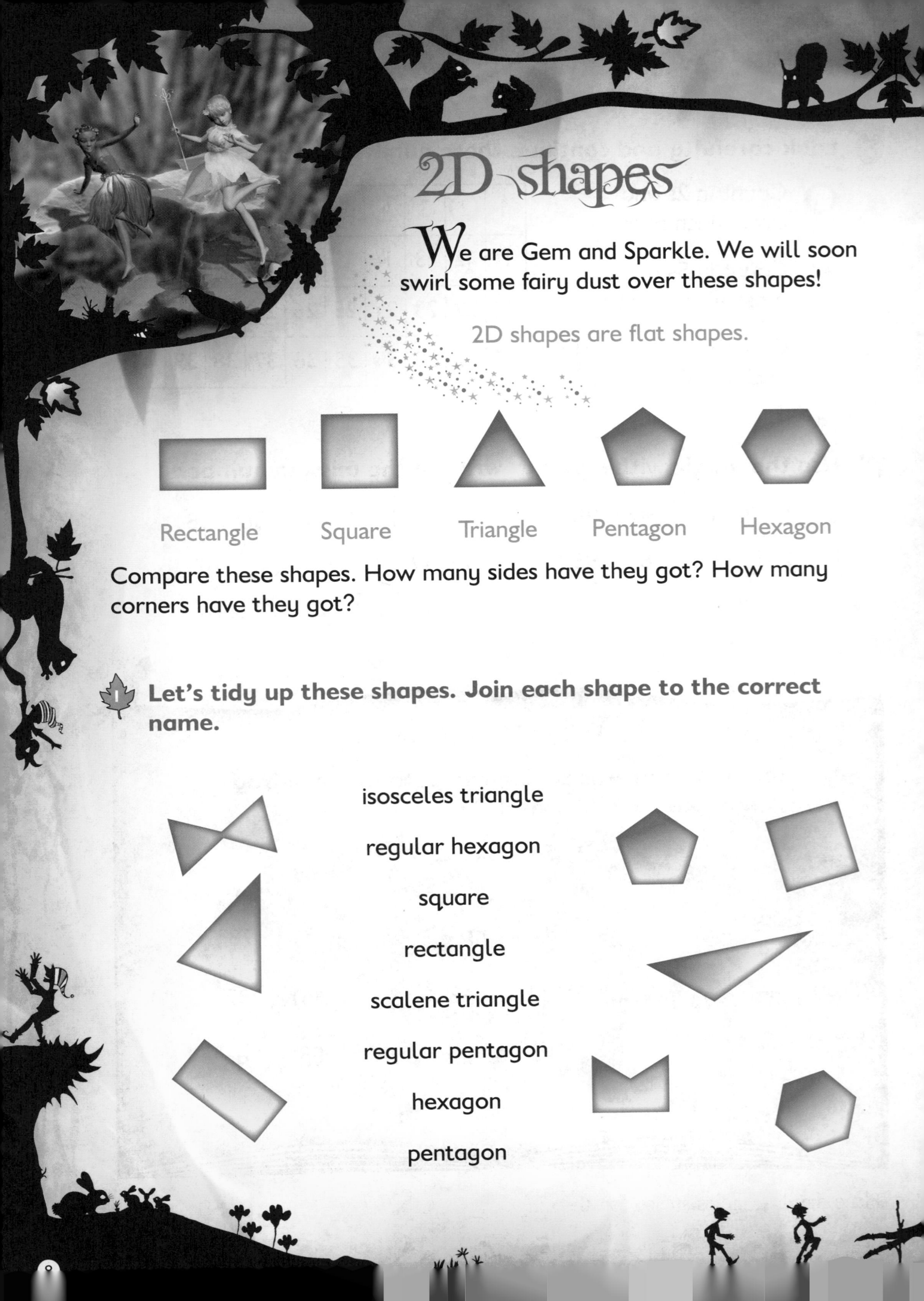

Rectangle   Square   Triangle   Pentagon   Hexagon

Compare these shapes. How many sides have they got? How many corners have they got?

Let's tidy up these shapes. Join each shape to the correct name.

isosceles triangle

regular hexagon

square

rectangle

scalene triangle

regular pentagon

hexagon

pentagon

2 Wave your wand and write the name for each of these.

a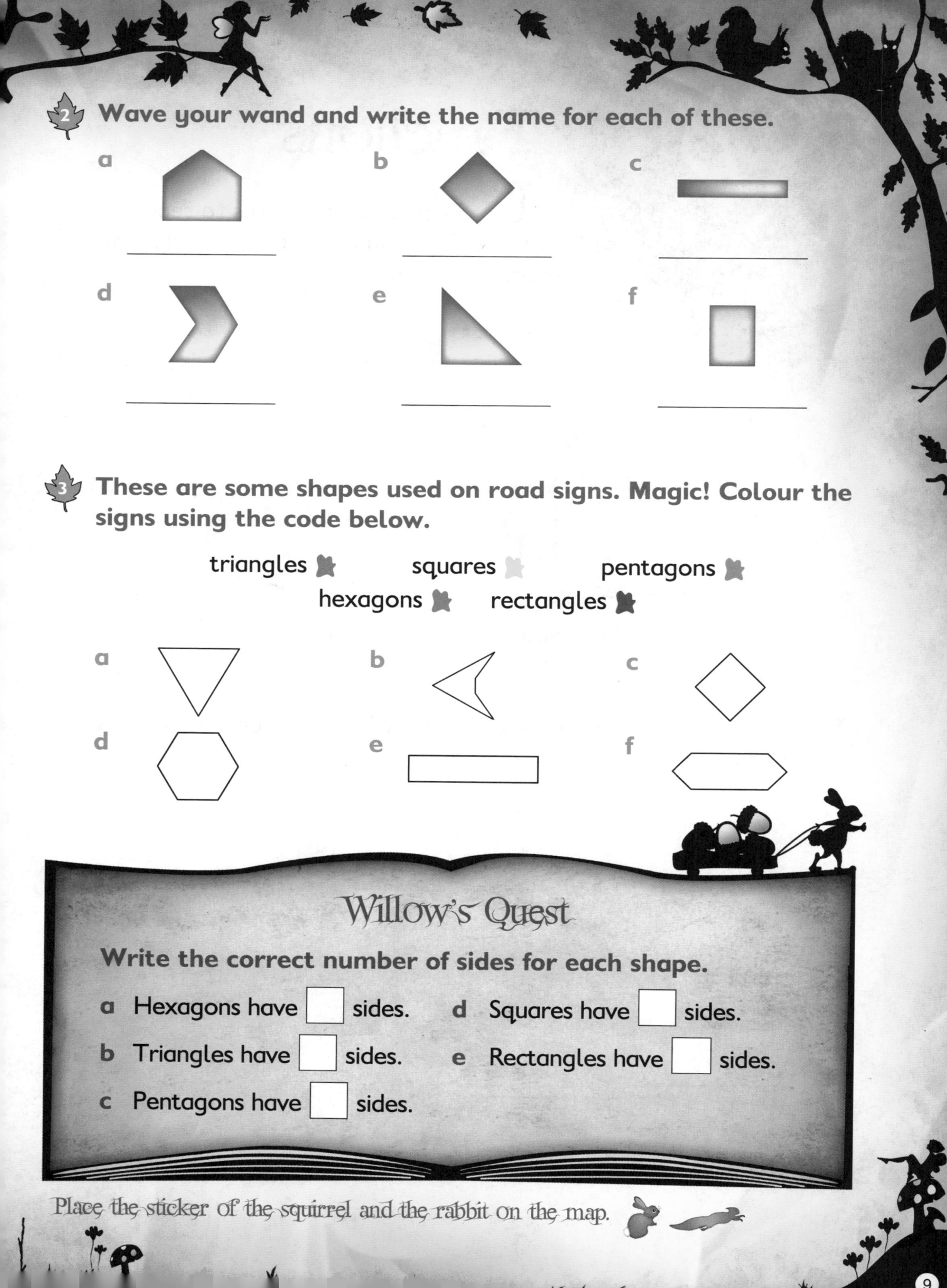

b

c

_____

d

e

f

_____

3 These are some shapes used on road signs. Magic! Colour the signs using the code below.

triangles ✦   squares ✦   pentagons ✦
hexagons ✦   rectangles ✦

a

b

c

d

e

f

Willow's Quest

Write the correct number of sides for each shape.

a Hexagons have ☐ sides.   d Squares have ☐ sides.

b Triangles have ☐ sides.   e Rectangles have ☐ sides.

c Pentagons have ☐ sides.

Place the sticker of the squirrel and the rabbit on the map.

Fractions

I am Finn. It is time for us to search for the truth behind fractions. Fractions are equal parts of a whole.

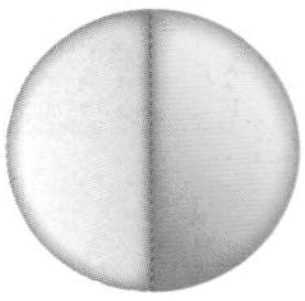

One half ($\frac{1}{2}$) is shaded.

Two equal parts are halves.

Quarter ($\frac{1}{4}$)   Not quarter

Four equal parts are quarters.

1 **Can you focus on these fractions? Write half or quarter for each shape.**

a _____

d _____

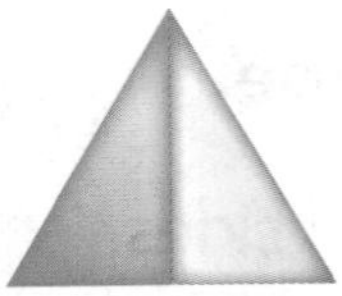

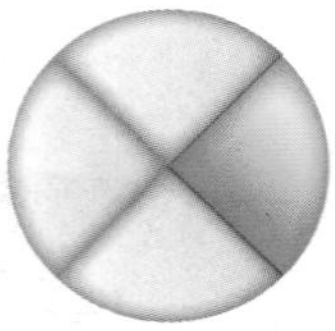

b _____

e _____

c _____

f _____

2 Now try these, fractions warrior. Colour $\frac{1}{2}$ of each shape.

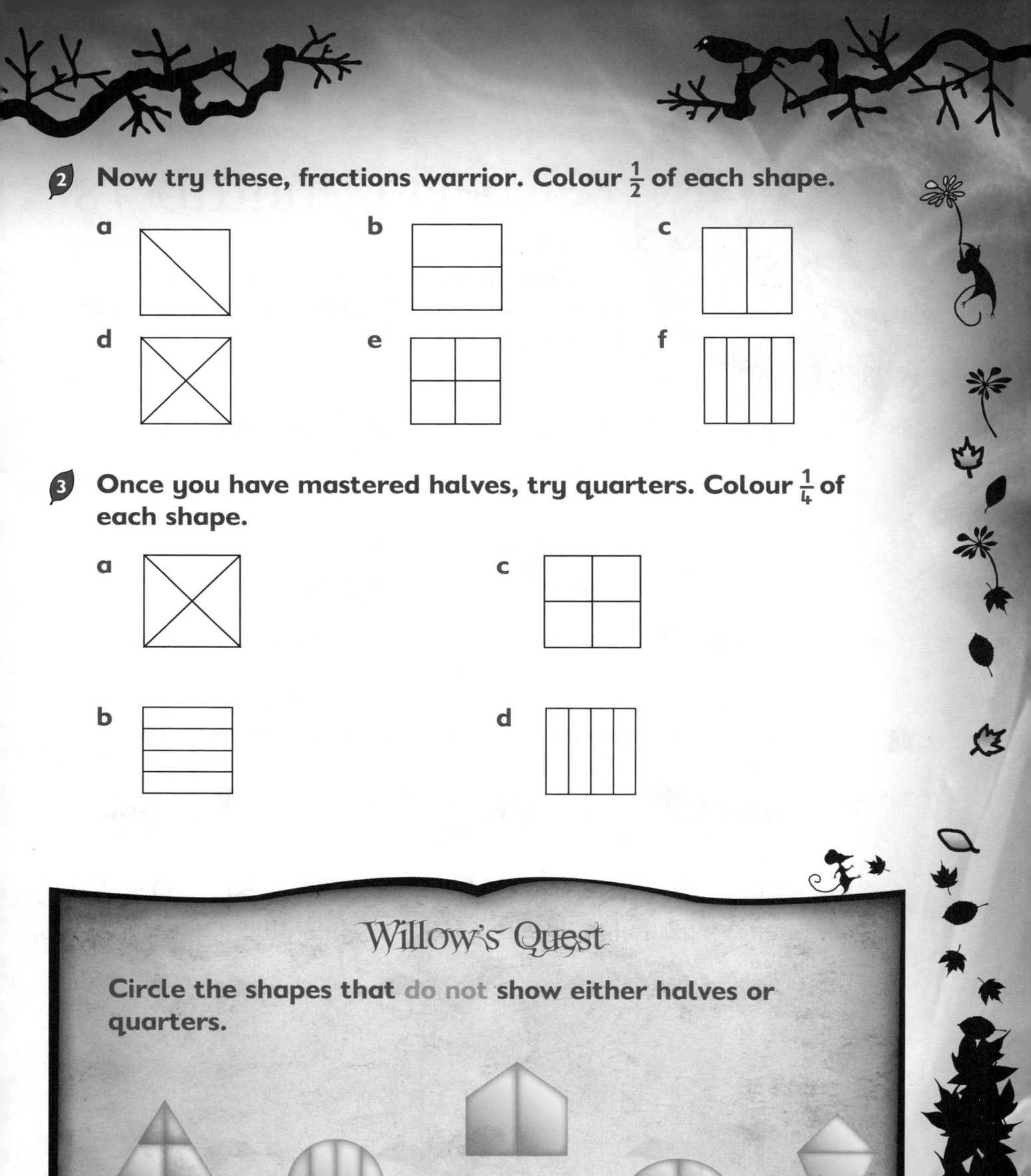

a

b

c

d

e

f

3 Once you have mastered halves, try quarters. Colour $\frac{1}{4}$ of each shape.

a

c

b

d

Willow's Quest

Circle the shapes that do not show either halves or quarters.

Place the sticker of the hedgehogs gathering food on the map.

Ordering numbers

When you put 2-digit numbers in order, look at the tens and then the ones digit. Use this number line to help.

0   10   20   30   40   50   60   70   80   90   100

39

63

63 is larger than 39, because 6 tens is more than 3 tens. **Bugalicious!**

⭐ **Draw a line from each bat to the matching place on the number line.**

a

55   29   93

0   10   20   30   40   50   60   70   80   90   100

32   68   86

b

27   34   48

0   50

2 Bring on the bugs! Circle the owl with the largest number in each pair. Gribbit is the largest out of us pair of pixies!

a   46   81   b   27   53   c   90   19

d   32   23   e   67   76   f   54   58

3 Try these pongy problems. Write each set of numbers in order, starting with the smallest.

a   71   38   25   64   smallest ☐ ☐ ☐ ☐

b   92   99   90   93   smallest ☐ ☐ ☐ ☐

c   54   14   44   51   smallest ☐ ☐ ☐ ☐

d   87   77   88   78   smallest ☐ ☐ ☐ ☐

Willow's Quest

Write all of the 2-digit numbers that can be made from the digits 1, 2 and 3. Write them in order, starting with the smallest. Use each number only once in each two-digit number.

1 **2** **3**

smallest   largest

☐☐   ☐☐   ☐☐   ☐☐   ☐☐   ☐☐

Place the owl sticker on the map.

Pearl's wisdom

1 **Read these carefully and write in the numbers.**

a thirty-five ☐

b seventy ☐

c twenty-one ☐

d ninety-eight ☐

e forty-six ☐

f fifty-five ☐

2 **Use the magic within you to complete the addition and subtraction facts for these trios.**

a 5 6 11

$5 + 6 = \boxed{}$ $\boxed{} - 5 = 6$

$\boxed{} + 5 = 11$ $11 - \boxed{} = 5$

b 17 8 9

$8 + \boxed{} = 17$ $17 - \boxed{} = 9$

$9 + \boxed{} = 17$ $17 - \boxed{} = 8$

3 **Take your time and count in 2s, 5s or 10s. Write the next two numbers in each counting pattern.**

a 37 39 41 43 ◯ ◯

b 74 79 84 89 ◯ ◯

c 22 32 42 52 ◯ ◯

d 60 62 64 66 ◯ ◯

4 You can do this with a swish of your tail! Draw a line to match each shape with its name and its number of sides.

square   3 sides

triangle   4 sides

hexagon

pentagon   5 sides

rectangle   6 sides

5 Circle the correct answer, $\frac{1}{2}$, $\frac{1}{4}$ or not $\frac{1}{2}$ or $\frac{1}{4}$ for each shape. Just do your best!

a $\frac{1}{2}$ b $\frac{1}{2}$ c $\frac{1}{2}$
      $\frac{1}{4}$ $\frac{1}{4}$ $\frac{1}{4}$
   not $\frac{1}{2}$ or $\frac{1}{4}$ not $\frac{1}{2}$ or $\frac{1}{4}$ not $\frac{1}{2}$ or $\frac{1}{4}$

d $\frac{1}{2}$ e $\frac{1}{2}$ f $\frac{1}{2}$
      $\frac{1}{4}$ $\frac{1}{4}$ $\frac{1}{4}$
   not $\frac{1}{2}$ or $\frac{1}{4}$ not $\frac{1}{2}$ or $\frac{1}{4}$ not $\frac{1}{2}$ or $\frac{1}{4}$

6 Write these numbers in order, starting with the smallest. The Lake of Wisdom holds the answers.

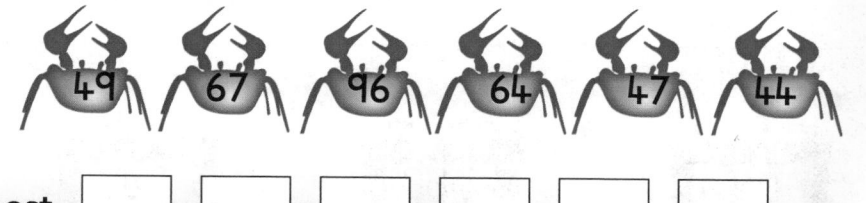

49   67   96   64   47   44

smallest

Place the sticker of pearls and shells on the map.

Reading the time

Clocks – what marvellous inventions!
Remember – there are 60 minutes in an
hour. Tick-tock!

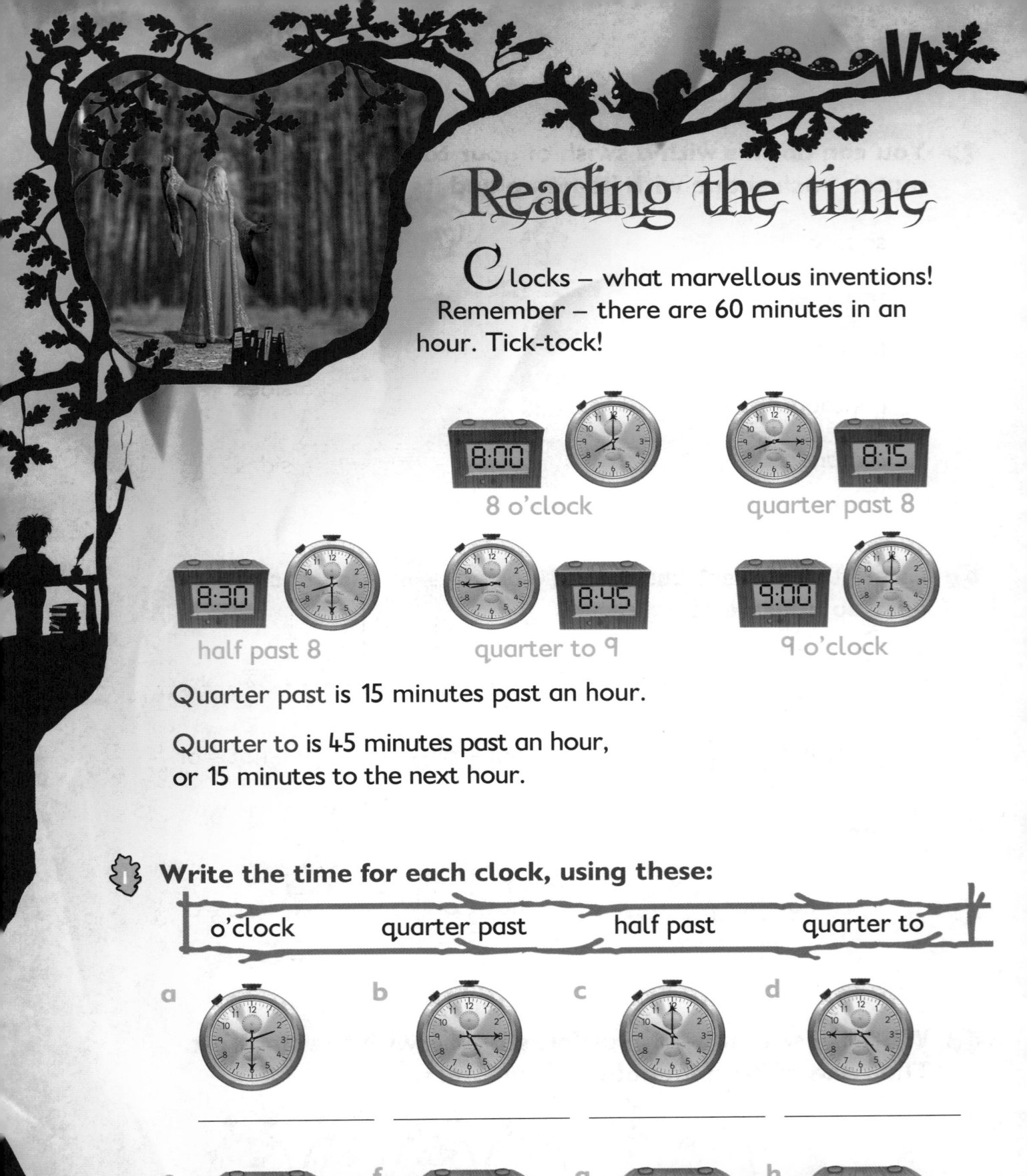

8:00 — 8 o'clock

8:15 — quarter past 8

8:30 — half past 8

8:45 — quarter to 9

9:00 — 9 o'clock

Quarter past is **15** minutes past an hour.

Quarter to is **45** minutes past an hour,
or **15** minutes to the next hour.

Write the time for each clock, using these:

o'clock	quarter past	half past	quarter to

a
b
c
d

e 11:45
f 3:00
g 6:30
h 12:15

Enchanted Forest Map Stickers

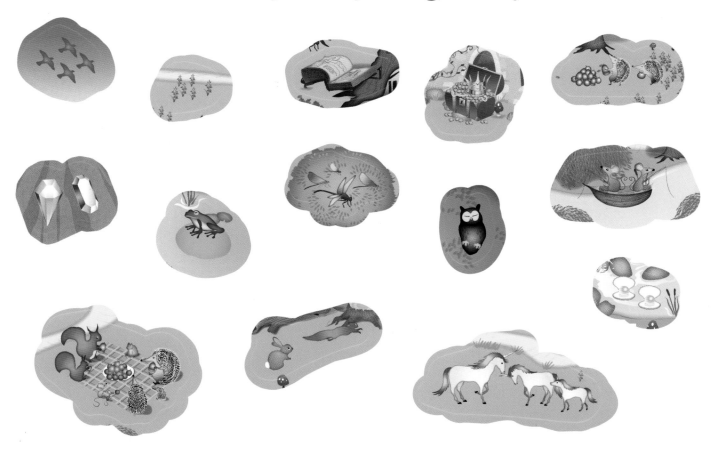

Extra Stickers

Forest Friends

 Join the matching clocks. It is as easy as 1-2-3!

 Write the times on each of these digital clocks. No time like the present!

a

1 o'clock

b

quarter past 11

c

12 o'clock

d

quarter to 6

e

half past 3

f

quarter to 8

Willow's Quest

Wonderful work! Now join the clock with the correct time to each of my appointments.

Dear Professor Willow, Please come to my cave at 4 o'clock to see my new invention. Yours, Finn

A music concert at quarter past 5.

Aurora is taking me to the Glade of Yesterday at quarter to 6.

You are invited to the Enchanted Ball! Arrive at half past 7.

Place the woodland picnic sticker on the map. Tick-tock!

Adding

We are Dusty and Firefly. Did you know that you can break numbers up so that you can add them in your head? Magic!

What is 34 add 5?

$34 + 5 =$

$30 + 4 + 5 =$

$30 + 4 + 5 = 39$

Add the ones and then add this to the tens.

Add together 23 and 40.

$23 + 40 =$

$20 + 3 + 40 =$

$20 + 40 + 3 = 63$

Add the tens and then add on the ones.

Wave your wand and break these numbers up to help you answer the sums.

a $17 + 2 =$

$10 + 7 + 2 =$

b $23 + 6 =$

$20 + 3 + 6 =$

c $52 + 4 =$

$50 + 2 + 4 =$

d $48 + 20 =$

$40 + 8 + 20 =$

e $39 + 50 =$

$30 + 9 + 50 =$

f $67 + 30 =$

$60 + 7 + 30 =$

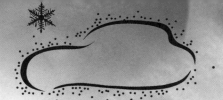

2 Swirl some fairy dust over these sums and write the answers.

a 43 + 3 =

b 61 + 7 =

c 52 + 5 =

d 26 + 20 =

e 19 + 70 =

f 38 + 40 =

3 Now read these and write the answers.

a Gribbit has 35 arrows and Periwinkle has
   30 arrows. How many arrows do the pixies
   have altogether?   _____

b Aurora has 42 objects in her nest at the top
   of the oak tree. She has found 6 new objects.
   How many does she have in total?   _____

c Professor Willow has completed 94 pages in
   his Book of Knowledge and there are 5 pages
   left. How many pages are there altogether?   _____

d Pearl flew 28km beyond the Enchanted Forest
   and 40km back to the Lake of Wisdom.
   How far did she fly in total?   _____

Willow's Quest

**Complete this
addition grid.**

+	4	30	60	5
24	28			
32		62		37
13			73	

Place the sticker of the crystals on the map. Flit, flit!

Taking away

Purr, purr! I am Aurora. Did you know that you can break numbers up so that you can subtract them in your head?

What is 37 subtract 5?

$$37 - 5 =$$

$$30 + 7 - 5 =$$

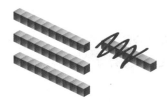

$$30 + 7 - 5 = 32$$

Subtract the ones.
Then add this to the tens.

Take away 30 from 54.

$$54 - 30 =$$

$$50 + 4 - 30 =$$

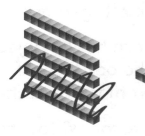

$$50 - 30 = 20 + 4 = 24$$

Subtract the tens.
Then add on the ones.

1 Break the numbers up to help you take away.

a $49 - 3 =$
$40 + 9 - 3 =$

b $65 - 4 =$
$60 + 5 - 4 =$

c $78 - 6 =$
$70 + 8 - 6 =$

d $91 - 20 =$
$90 + 1 - 20 =$

e $64 - 30 =$
$60 + 4 - 30 =$

f $83 - 40 =$
$80 + 3 - 40 =$

2 The sky is the limit with take away trails! Subtract and write in the answers.

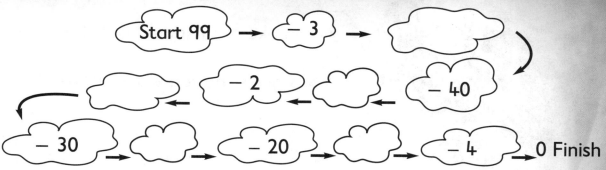

Start 99 → − 3 → [ ]

− 40 ← [ ] ← − 2 ← [ ]

− 30 → [ ] → − 20 → [ ] → − 4 → 0 Finish

3 You are flying through this! Read and answer these.

a Take 30 away from 57.

_____

b Subtract 4 from 66.

_____

c What is 73 take away 20?

_____

d What is 5 less than 29?

_____

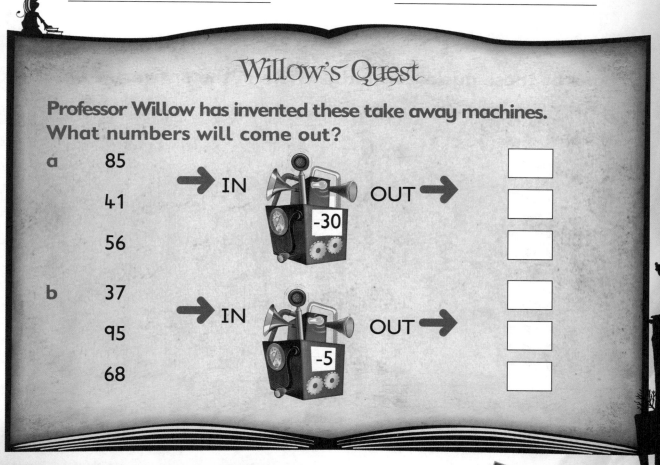

Willow's Quest

Professor Willow has invented these take away machines.
What numbers will come out?

a   85
41   IN   OUT
56   -30

b   37
95   IN   OUT
68   -5

  Place the treasure chest sticker on the map. You are a star!

21

Multiplication

The Lake of Wisdom holds the answers.

4 x 3 gives the same answer as 3 x 4.

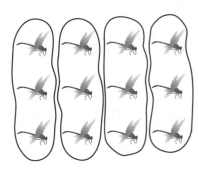

4 multiplied by 3 = 12

4 x 3 = 12

4 + 4 + 4 = 12

3 multiplied by 4 = 12

3 x 4 = 12

3 + 3 + 3 + 3 = 12

1 **Look at these ducks carefully. Write in the answers.**

a

4 + 4 = ☐

2 x 4 = ☐

b

3 + 3 + 3 + 3 + 3 = ☐

5 x 3 = ☐

c

4 + 4 + 4 + 4 = ☐

4 x 4 = ☐

d

2 + 2 + 2 = ☐

3 x 2 = ☐

2 Draw five spots on each frog. Use the magic within you to multiply and write the answer.

a  3 x 5 = ▢

b  2 x 5 = ▢

c  4 x 5 = ▢

3 Write the answers to these multiplications. You can do this with a swish of your tail!

a 2 x 4 = ▢   b 3 x 6 = ▢   c 3 x 5 = ▢
  4 x 2 = ▢   6 x 3 = ▢   5 x 3 = ▢

d 2 x 5 = ▢   e 3 x 2 = ▢   f 1 x 4 = ▢
  5 x 2 = ▢   2 x 3 = ▢   4 x 1 = ▢

Willow's Quest

Complete the Book of Knowledge by multiplying each of these. Write the answer and colour the lily pad which is the odd one out.

a 3 x 4 = ◯   b 6 x 2 = ◯   c 2 x 4 = ◯

d 4 x 3 = ◯   e 2 x 6 = ◯

Swish, swish! Place the frog sticker on the map.

3D shapes

3D shapes are solid shapes.
Wave your wand and compare these shapes.

Cuboid   Cube   Sphere   Cone   Cylinder   Pyramid

Look at the faces of each shape.
This cube has 6 square faces.

face

❋ **Let's tidy up this cupboard. Join each shape to the correct word.**

cuboid

cube

sphere

cone

cylinder

pyramid

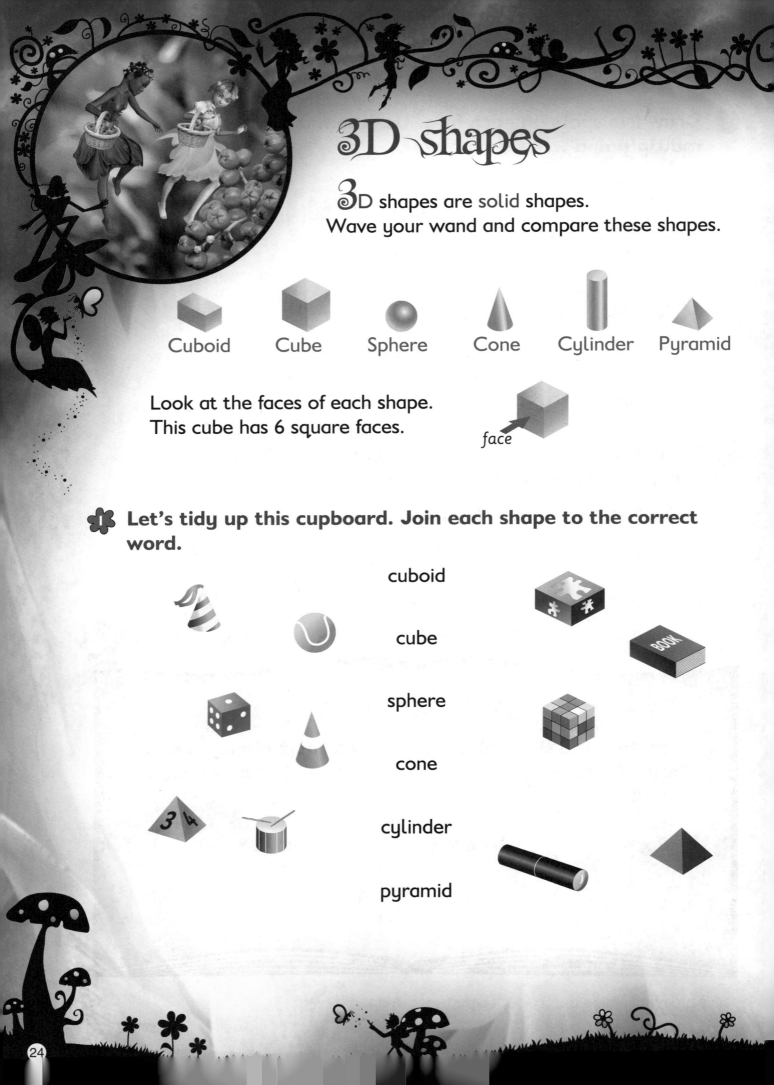

2 Swirl some fairy dust over these shapes and write the name for each group.

a  _____

b  _____

c _____

d  _____

e  _____

f  _____

3 Flit, flit! Circle True or False for each of these sentences.

a A pyramid has some faces that are triangles.   True   False

b A cube has 6 square faces.   True   False

c A cylinder has 6 faces.   True   False

d A cuboid has 8 faces.   True   False

Willow's Quest

Tick the right columns to complete this magic shape chart.

Shape name	Has rectangle or square faces	Has a triangle face	Has a circle face
Cube			
Cuboid			
Cylinder			
Cone			

Place the bluebells sticker on the map.

Measuring length

A ruler is a useful tool for measuring smaller lengths. It is as easy as 1-2-3! This shows a centimetre ruler.

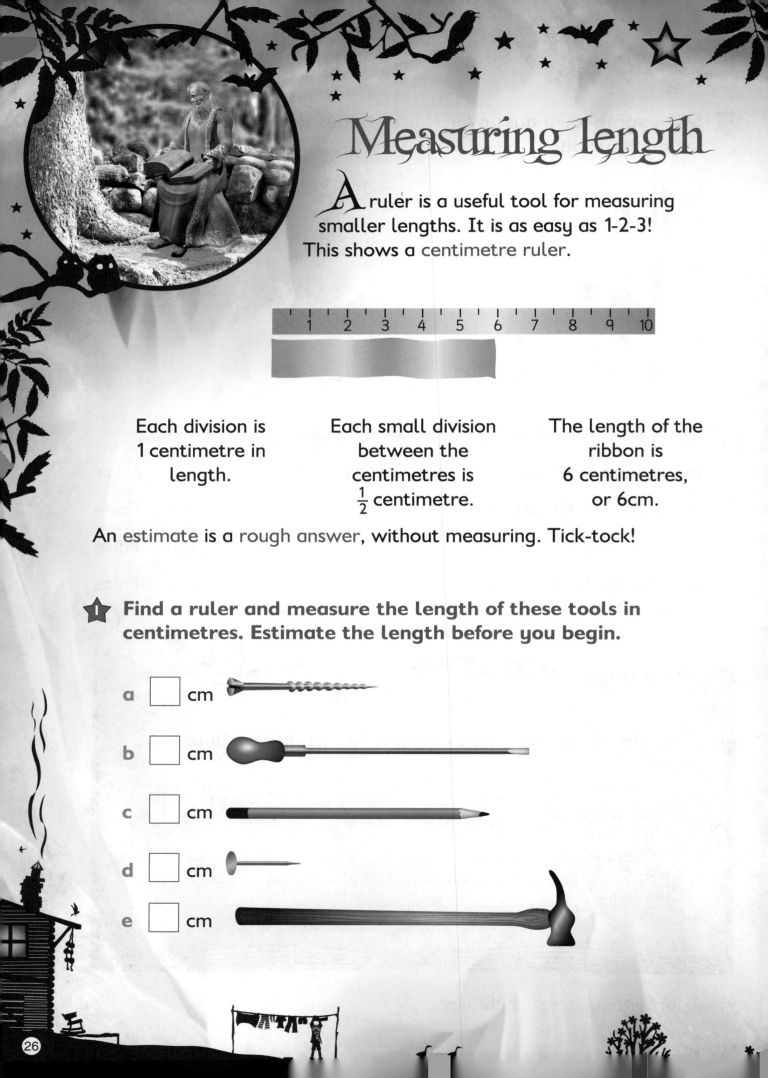

| 1 | 2 | 3 | 4 | 5 | 6 | 7 | 8 | 9 | 10 |

Each division is 1 centimetre in length.

Each small division between the centimetres is $\frac{1}{2}$ centimetre.

The length of the ribbon is 6 centimetres, or 6cm.

An **estimate** is a rough answer, without measuring. Tick-tock!

⭐ **Find a ruler and measure the length of these tools in centimetres. Estimate the length before you begin.**

a [ ] cm

b [ ] cm

c [ ] cm

d [ ] cm

e [ ] cm

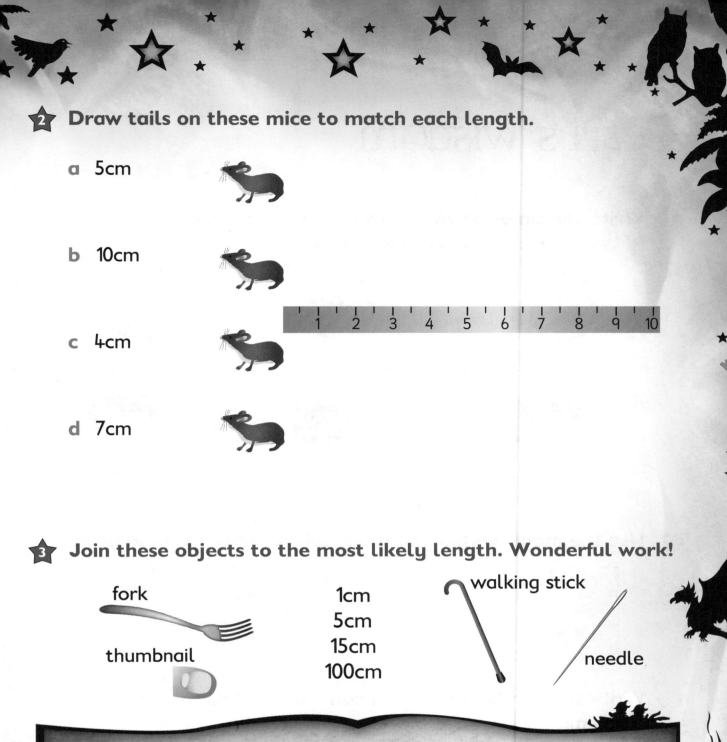

2 Draw tails on these mice to match each length.

a 5cm

b 10cm

c 4cm

d 7cm

3 Join these objects to the most likely length. Wonderful work!

fork

thumbnail

1cm
5cm
15cm
100cm

walking stick

needle

Willow's Quest

Measure the length of one side and all the way round this square. If at first you do not succeed, try, try again!

a Length of one side is ＿＿ cm.

b Length all the way round is ＿＿ cm.

Place the birds sticker on the map.

Pearl's wisdom

1 Write the times on these clocks. Use **o'clock**, **quarter past**, **half past** or **quarter to**. Take your time.

a

_____

b

_____

c

_____

d

_____

e

_____

f

_____

2 Use the magic within you to complete these addition grids.

a

+	20	50
34		
47		97

b

+	63	54
5	68	
3		

3 Write the numbers that will come out of this take away machine.

a   73

b   86

c   61

d   49

e   36

f   58

 IN → OUT →

-30

4 **Write the answers to these multiplications. You can do this with a swish of your tail!**

a 3 x 3 = ☐   d 2 x 2 = ☐

b 5 x 2 = ☐   e 2 x 4 = ☐

c 3 x 4 = ☐   f 3 x 5 = ☐

5 **Look carefully and write the name of the odd shape out in each set.**

a

The odd shape out is a

_____ .

c

The odd shape out is a

_____ .

b

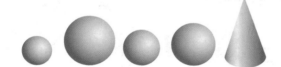

The odd shape out is a

_____ .

d

The odd shape out is a

_____ .

6 **Swish, swish! Measure the length of the seaweed.**

a _____ cm

b _____ cm

c _____ cm

Place the unicorns sticker on the map.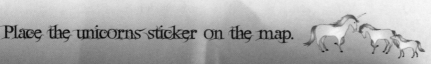

Answers

Pages 2–3

1
a eighty
b twelve
c thirty
d twenty-six
e seventy-five
f ninety-one
g nineteen
h fifty-seven

(boxes: 12, 30, 75, 80, 57, 91, 19, 26)

2 a

20	21	22	23
30	31	32	33
40	41	42	43

b

76	77	78	79
86	87	88	89
96	97	98	99

3
a 45
b 10
c 69
d 50

Willow's Quest

Crossword:
- a seventy
- b thirty
- c fifty
- d twenty
- e ninety
- f eighty
- g forty
- (down) sixty, ninety

Pages 4–5

1
a 14, 14, 14, 14
b 7, 7, 6, 6
c 7, 7, 7, 7

2
a 8, 8
b 5, 5
c 8, 8
d 11, 11

3
a 4 + 5 = 9, 9 − 4 = 5 or 9 − 5 = 4
b 8 + 5 = 13, 13 − 8 = 5 or 13 − 5 = 8
c 7 + 7 = 14, 14 − 7 = 7
d 6 + 12 = 18, 18 − 6 = 12 or 18 − 12 = 6

Willow's Quest

4 + 7 = 11   12 − 6 = 6   2 + 13 = 15
5 − 3 = 2   7 + 3 = 10   18 − 4 = 14

Pages 6–7

1
a 15, 17, 19
b 54, 56, 58
c 28, 33, 38
d 82, 87, 92
e 45, 55, 65
f 79, 89, 99

2

1	②	3	④	5̶	⑥	7	⑧	9	⑩
11	⑫	13	⑭	1̶5̶	⑯	17	⑱	19	⑳
21	㉒	23	㉔	25	㉖	27	㉘	29	㉚
31	㉜	33	㉞	3̶5̶	㊱	37	㊳	39	㊵

3
a 95   d 30
b 65   e 62
c 66   f 11

Willow's Quest

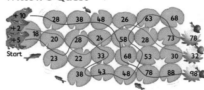

Pages 8–9

1
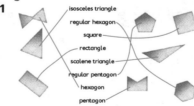

isosceles triangle
regular hexagon
square
rectangle
scalene triangle
regular pentagon
hexagon
pentagon

2
a pentagon   d hexagon
b square   e triangle
c rectangle   f rectangle

3 Coloured as follows:
a red   d blue
b green   e brown
c yellow   f blue

Willow's Quest
a 6
b 3
c 5
d 4
e 4

Pages 10–11

1
a half
b half
c quarter
d quarter
e half
f quarter

2 a
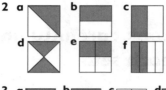

3 a
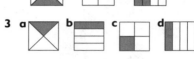

Willow's Quest

The triangle, the circle and the kite are not divided into exact halves or quarters.

Pages 12–13

1
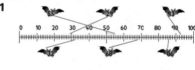

2
a 81   d 32
b 53   e 76
c 90   f 58

3
a 25, 38, 64, 71
b 90, 92, 93, 99
c 14, 44, 51, 54
d 77, 78, 87, 88

Willow's Quest
12, 13, 21, 23, 31, 32

Pages 14–15

1
a 35
b 70
c 21
d 98
e 46
f 55

2
a 5 + 6 = 11   11 − 5 = 6
  6 + 5 = 11   11 − 6 = 5
b 8 + 9 = 17   17 − 8 = 9
  9 + 8 = 17   17 − 9 = 8

3
a 45, 47
b 94, 99

c 62, 72
d 68, 70

4

5 a $\frac{1}{4}$
b $\frac{1}{2}$
c not $\frac{1}{2}$ or $\frac{1}{4}$
d $\frac{1}{4}$
e not $\frac{1}{2}$ or $\frac{1}{4}$
f $\frac{1}{2}$

6 44, 47, 49, 64, 67, 96

Pages 16–17

1 a half past 2
b quarter past 5
c 10 o'clock
d quarter to 5
e quarter to 12
f 3 o'clock
g half past 6
h quarter past 12

2

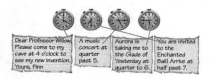

3 a 1.00   **d** 5.45
b 11.15   **e** 3.30
c 12.00   **f** 7.45

Willow's Quest

Dear Professor Willow, Please come to my cave at 4 o'clock to see my new invention. Yours, Finn | A music concert at quarter past 5. | Aurora is taking me to the Glade of Yesterday at quarter to 6. | You are invited to the Enchanted Ball. Arrive at half past 7.

Pages 18–19

1 a 19, 19
b 29, 29
c 56, 56
d 68, 68
e 89, 89
f 97, 97
2 a 46
b 68
c 57
d 46
e 89
f 78
3 a 65
b 48
c 99
d 68km

Willow's Quest

+	4	30	60	5
24	28	54	84	29
32	36	62	92	37
13	17	43	73	18

Pages 20–21

1 a 46, 46
b 61, 61
c 72, 72
d 71, 71
e 34, 34
f 43, 43
2 96, 56, 54, 24, 4
3 a 27
b 62
c 53
d 24

Willow's Quest

a 55, 11, 26
b 32, 90, 63

Pages 22–23

1 a 8, 8
b 15, 15
c 16, 16
d 6, 6
2 a 15
b 10
c 20
3 a 8, 8
b 18, 18
c 15, 15
d 10, 10
e 6, 6
f 4, 4

Willow's Quest

The odd one out is 2 x 4. All of the others have 12 as the answer.

Pages 24–25

1

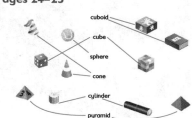

2 a cylinders
b cuboids
c pyramids
d spheres
e cubes
f cones
3 a True
b True

c False
d False

Willow's Quest

Pages 26 – 27

1 a 4cm
b 8cm
c 7cm
d 2cm
e 9cm
2 Check that the lines are drawn to the exact length.
3

1cm
5cm
15cm
100cm

Willow's Quest

a 2cm
b 8cm

Pages 28–29

1 a quarter past 1
b quarter to 6
c 12 o'clock
d half past 3
e quarter to 11
f quarter past 9

2 a

+	20	50
34	54	84
47	67	97

b

+	63	54
5	68	59
3	66	57

3 a 43   **d** 19
b 56   **e** 6
c 31   **f** 28
4 a 9   **d** 4
b 10   **e** 8
c 12   **f** 15
5 a cylinder
b cone
c cube
d pyramid
6 a 6cm
b 9cm
c 8cm

Welcome to the Enchanted Forest...

Wonderful work!